Tarns of the Fells

Celebrating Cumbria's mountain landscapes

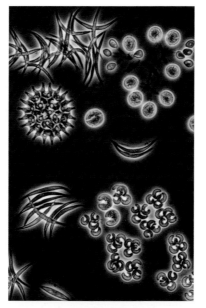

Flora of the Fells Project

Cover photograph: Innominate Tarn (Keith Wood). Insets: pond skater, water flea, great diving beetle (Freshwater Biological Association), common toad (Cumbria Wildlife Trust)

Overleaf: Bleaberry Tarn (Keith Wood), phytoplankton (Hilda Canter-Lund), Blea Water (Dave Willis)

Text contributors: Jane Armstrong, Elizabeth Haworth, Robert Holland, Phil Jelfs, Joe Murphy, Jackie Oglesby, Simon Pawley, Anne Powell, Izzy Thorne, Joanna Varley, Martin Varley

Design: Martin Varley

Photography: Jane Armstrong (31, 31 inset), Hilda Canter-Lund (27 far left), Cumbria Tourist Board/Ben Barden (12, 30), Cumbria Wildlife Trust (27 far right, inside back cover bottom right), English Nature/Paul Glendell (5,17 right), English Nature/Peter Wakeley (19 bottom left, 35 right), Freshwater Biological Association (19 top left, 21 top, 21 bottom, 22, 26 left, 26 right, 27 far left, 27 middle left, 27 middle, 27 middle right, 29 top, 29 bottom left, 40), Roger Hiley (41), Tony Marshall (19 top right, 19 bottom right, 29 bottom right, inside back cover bottom right), Martin Varley (10 left, 10 right, 13, 14, 25, 33, 38), Dave Willis/www.mountainsportsphoto.com (3, 6, 8, 17 left, 23, 32, 34, 35 left, inside back cover top), Keith Woods (9, 10 middle, 15, 16, 20, 37, 39)

Illustrations on pages 4 and 42: Joanna Varley

Maps on pages 4 and 11 reproduced under copyright licence number 100033062

Tarn charts on page 10 and other tarns data are reproduced from *Tarns of the Central Lake District*, by kind permission of the Brathay Exploration Group Trust

Quotes from W. Heaton Cooper's *The Tarns of Lakeland* reproduced courtesy of Heaton Cooper Family

© 2005 Friends of the Lake District

ISBN: 0-9540506-3-0

For further information about the Flora of the Fells Project please contact:
Martin Varley, Flora of the Fells Project Officer, c/o Friends of the Lake District, Murley Moss, Oxenholme Road, Kendal, Cumbria, LA9 7SS
Tel: 01539 720788
E-mail: martin-varley@fld.org.uk
Website: www.floraofthefells.com

Contents

Stickle Tarn with climber on Pavey Ark

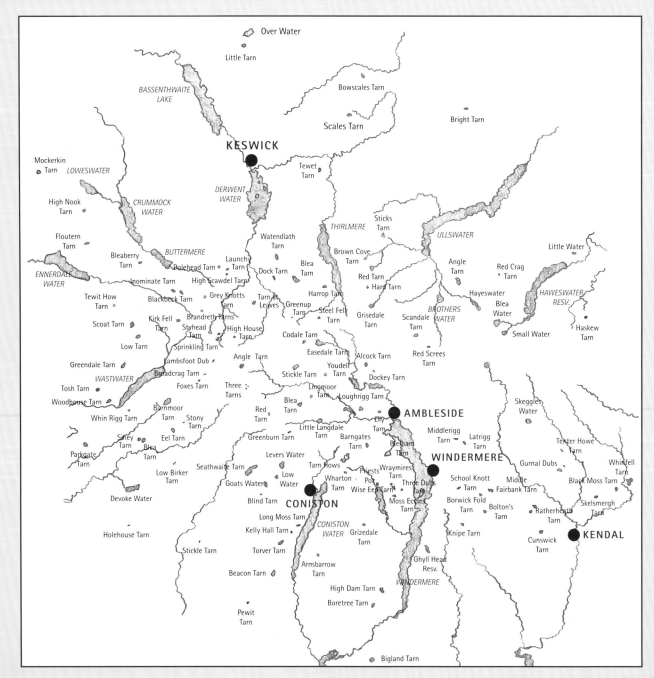

Tarns of the fells

Foreword

The high fells of Lakeland are enriched by their tarns. Mirroring the crags and the clouds, they add a special dimension to the landscape. It is hard to imagine Lakeland without them. And they are not only jewels set in clasps of crag, but the stuff of legend. In William Wordsworth's *Song at the Feast of Brougham Castle,* when Henry Clifford, 'the Shepherd Lord', was hiding from his hereditary enemies amid the Troutbeck fells:

> *'Both the undying fish that swim*
> *Through Bowscale Tarn did wait on him.'*

According to Sir Walter Scott in *The Bridal of Triermain,* dark under Blencathra, Scales Tarn was reputed to be eternally shaded:

> *'Never sunbeam could discern*
> *The surface of that sable tarn*
> *In whose black mirror you may spy*
> *The stars, while noontide lights the sky.'*

Was this, indeed, the origin of J R R Tolkien's Mirrormere, where stars glittered in the deep even at high noon? Artists, too, have found the tarns compulsive subjects. The celebrated local painter W. Heaton Cooper called them 'the eyes of the mountains' and they feature in many of his stylised compositions, known all over the world.

For the scientists and naturalists the tarns are a source of other fascinations. Many of the highest and most spectacular occupy cirques scooped from the fells by ice and some are surprisingly deep. Blea Water on High Street, has a depth of 63 metres, only surpassed by Wastwater and Windermere, and is the finest example of a cirque lake in England. Other tarns owe their existence to glacial moraines that have dammed valley head streams – not necessarily forever, as the drainage of Keppel Cove

Tarn on Helvellyn when its dam was breached after a cloudburst in 1927 reminds us. Some have trapped in their sediments the record of changes in climate and flora since the ice age, chronicling the clearance of forests, the spread of agriculture and the deposition of radioactive isotopes released from Chernobyl in the 1980s. While the biodiversity of the high-level tarns is low, reflecting the lack of nutrients in such young, rock-girt and cold waters, because of their coldness, purity and isolation many retain species that are rare elsewhere.

The tarns are diverse. Those set in high rock basins – like Angle Tarn, Blea Water, Red Tarn or Scales Tarn – may be the most spectacular, but lower and more richly vegetated waters like Loughrigg Tarn, Little Langdale Tarn or Blelham Tarn enrich the landscape of the dale floors, alongside the smaller lakes, which are themselves little more than big, valley-bottom, tarns.

Wordsworth called our region 'the District of the Lakes in the North of England'. But the great and famous lakes are vastly outnumbered by the lesser waters – the hundreds of tarns which also give so much character and beauty to England's most famous and most cherished landscape. This little book, produced by a partnership of independent trusts with sponsorship from English Nature, seeks to raise people's awareness of these waters and explain both their importance and their vulnerability. I hope that it will inspire you to seek out these 'eyes of the mountains' – and see the hills with a new vision. Your purchase will help support the charities who are working to conserve our upland scenery and habitats and ensure that Lakeland passes unscathed to future generations.

Sir Martin Holdgate CB,
President of the Freshwater Biological Association

Low Water, Coniston. Levers Water is just in view in the distance

Tarns of the fells

Many people know Cumbria because of its lakes. Yet there are many more tarns than lakes. Cumbria is one of the most important counties in England for small water bodies like these. They are so common that it is easy to take them for granted and they have received less attention than other freshwater features like lakes and rivers. Across the country such small water bodies have disappeared through draining, ploughing and infilling. As they are lost so too are their treasures.

Tarn Tales: Levers Water

'As one leaves the Youth Hostel and begins to climb the last lap past Paddy End Mine to the tarn there is a choice of routes, one on either side of the beck. If the right hand side is chosen it is best to keep well up the fellside. The route on the opposite side crosses a scree shoot below several holes through the ridge where miners have excavated a natural weakness in the rock. This is called Simon's Nick, after a miner who discovered a rich vein of copper. The tale goes that success went to Simon's head, he boasted of his find, the Devil heard him and dried up the the vein of copper, and finally Simon met his end from a blast of gunpowder in his own mine'

'The Tarns of Lakeland' - W. Heaton Cooper

Tarns hold secrets from the past. They are a living legacy of how our landscape has evolved and a vital store of biodiversity, providing habitats for a wide range of plants and animals, from microscopic forms to fish and birds. They also add a dimension to the scenery. A sheet of perfect blue on a summer's day, they are oases of tranquillity; a flash of frozen white in winter, they are stark reminders of the changing seasons. Like diamonds sparkling amongst the fells, they possess an irresistible draw.

Scholars have long argued over the question of what is a tarn? The classic definition is a 'small mountain lake'. But the Vikings, who gave us the word when they described the Cumbrian landscape in which they settled 1100 years ago, knew nothing of classic definitions. They called any small body of water a 'tjörn', from which the word tarn is derived. It means 'a small lake', or more poetically 'a teardrop'. Look at local maps and from the salt marshes of the Solway Firth to the shoulders of Scafell Pike, apart from the main lakes, there is hardly a named patch of blue that is not called a tarn. Although the Scandinavians left a large legacy of place names across the north and east of England, tarns are unique to Cumbria and the neighbouring Yorkshire Dales.

For two hardy Grasmere men, Colin Dodgson and Tim Tyson, who spent their weekends in the 1960s bathing in more than 400 of them, a tarn was any mountain pool

A Taste of Tarns: **R e d T a r n**

Location: Under the eastern slopes of Helvellyn, tucked in between Striding Edge and Swirral Edge
Altitude: 719m
Depth: 26m
Area: 0.08km^2
pH: 6.6
Origin: Formed in a rock basin eroded by a small cirque glacier
Geology: Carved from the hard resistant volcanic rocks which dominate the central Lake District
Tarn Talk: Possibly one of the most well-known tarns of the fells, Red Tarn sits in a magnificent cirque formed as snow accumulated on the shady, northeast slopes of Helvellyn during the last ice age. Eventually enough snow built up to compress into ice, which then started to slip and rotate. This swivelling motion relentlessly plucked and gouged out a deep circular hollow. When temperatures rose, the glacier shrank away, filling the hollow with meltwater and dropping a dam of glacial debris or moraine across the lip. Although one of the highest tarns of the fells, records from pollen trapped in its sediments suggest that it was once surrounded by woodland of hazel, elm, oak and alder. Its fish include trout and the rare schelly, which is slim and silver like a herring.

deep enough to swim in. Some rigid thinkers say that a tarn must have a permanent outlet stream, but that would relegate many of the countless unnamed blue spots and dots that speckle the uplands to mere pools.

Since all of these slivers of water contribute so much to the life of our mountains, perhaps it would be better to say that any small body which possesses what we feel is the character of a tarn, and which we enjoy, we can call a tarn.

Tarn places

There are over two thousand tarns and pools in Cumbria. It is difficult to know the exact number because landscapes do not stand still. A hot summer dries up temporary tarns in stony basins or pans of peat. Under heavy rainfall hillwalkers may find themselves threading a path between strings of pools not marked on maps. Some tarns have disappeared altogether. Until 1927 there was a shallow tarn in Keppel Cove, north of Helvellyn, used as a water supply for local lead mines. During heavy rain the soil bank holding the water back was breached and the tarn drained completely. Now all that remains is a peaty hollow where the tarn used to lie.

Although found across Cumbria, tarns have become icons

Bleaberry Tarn, Red Pike, Buttermere

How ice carved a landscape – the making of Langdale's tarns

Little Langdale Tarn

Blea Tarn

Stickle Tarn

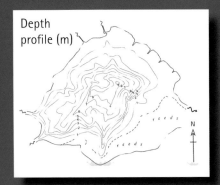

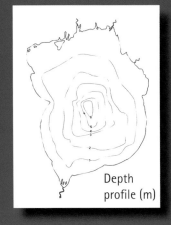

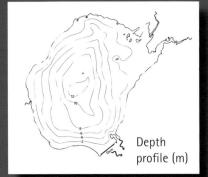

Stickle Tarn

Stickle Tarn lies in a cirque, a rock basin carved by a glacier, hanging high above the Great Langdale valley. Towering above the tarn is the imposing wall of Pavey Ark. Ice has roughened the terrain to the north and along its eastern edge are high moraines, debris left behind as the glacier retreated.

Near the outlet to Stickle Ghyll is a small dam which has raised the water level by about 2m. It was built in the nineteenth century to provide water power for the gunpowder works in Elterwater.

Blea Tarn

At the height of the last glaciation ice spilled over from the Great Langdale valley and flowed down into Little Langdale. As conditions warmed the glaciers retreated, leaving ice stranded on the col between the two valleys. The ice continued to erode the rock, deepening an ice-hollow probably formed by the glacier to create Blea Tarn.

The tarn has been free of ice for at least 14,000 years and studies of sediment on the tarn bed has allowed scientists to build up a picture of how the vegetation of the area has changed over that time.

Little Langdale Tarn

Little Langdale Tarn was formed where glaciers from Blea Tarn, Wrynose and Greenburn met. The combined force of ice would have provided the erosive energy needed to scour the basin in which the tarn now sits.

The tarn is shrinking and was perhaps once three times its present size. Greenburn Beck, which flows into the tarn, was dammed in the nineteenth century to provide water for the local copper industry, evidence for which is found in a copper-enriched layer of silt over 5cm thick in the tarn sediment.

Talkin Tarn, one of the few tarns in Cumbria which lie outside the Lake District

of the high fells, associated with remote, wilder places. The majority of tarns lie in the mountainous terrain of the Lake District National Park. Here hard, resistant, volcanic rocks dominate, underpinning the scenery of rugged relief and climbing crags for which the area is famous. The structure of these rocks is also susceptible to the erosional processes needed for tarns to form. They occur at all altitudes. Broadcrag Tarn, a stone's throw from the summit of Scafell Pike is the highest at over 800m, whilst Loughrigg Tarn is less than 100m above sea level.

Away from the central fells the geology changes. There are few tarns on the slaty, rocks north and west of Keswick,

which weather differently giving smoother, gentler scenery. Despite being similar in height to the central fells, the landscape of Skiddaw and Blencathra has only three tarns. Outside the Lake District rock types are different once again. Standing waters, like Blencow Tarn, near Penrith, or Talkin Tarn, east of Carlisle, are less frequent.

A band of limestone wraps around the Lake District to the south and east. Tarns sit uncomfortably here as limestone is permeable and does not hold water. Further east in the North Pennines there are only a handful of tarns scattered amongst hollows in the bogs.

A Taste of Tarns: D e v o k e W a t e r

Location: On the moorland uplands between Eskdale and Dunnerdale
Altitude: 244m
Depth: 16m
Area: 0.36 km²
pH: 6.3
Origin: It lies in a rocky hollow scoured out by a glacier descending from Birker Fell. As it retreated the ice left a bank of moraine across the valley which dammed meltwater to form the tarn
Geology: Sits close to where the Borrowdale volcanic rocks meet the granite of Eskdale
Tarn Talk: This large tarn has a long association with human activity. There are several prehistoric cairns around its shores and the Bronze Age settlement of Barnscar is close by. To the north at Brantrake Moss is evidence of ancient field systems associated with cultivation of cereals, which is thought to have taken place during Roman times. Sediment cores collected from the tarn bed have revealed information about vegetation changes going back 14,500 years. The tarn has a reputation as a good place for trout fishing. Perch, minnow and three-spined stickleback also occur here as well as freshwater limpet, leech and mayfly.

Most tarns in Cumbria, like Angle Tarn, Patterdale, pictured here, were formed as a result of glaciation

Tarn beginnings

Cumbria has a richly textured countryside. Upland slopes in the Lake District are pitted with hollows and valleys-bottoms broken by hummocks and mounds. The extraordinary concentration of tarns here owes everything to this intricately crafted and undulating landscape where water can be trapped and contained. Yet in geological terms tarns are young landscape features, formed during the last ice age that finally came to an end only about 10,000 years ago.

To see how ice, water and rock have created this landscape, stand by a tarn and imagine a glacier or ice sheet, maybe hundreds of metres thick, pressing down onto the ground beneath, freezing onto every knoll and outcrop. Then, as the ice moves under gravity, it tears out pieces of rock, some as small as sand grains, others as large as houses. This captured debris adds to the irresistible power of the ice, increasing its destructive force to scrape, plough and grind the bedrock.

Tarn Tales: **Bowscales Tarn**

'There is a legend that tells of two immortal fish that lived in the tarn. Fair Ermengarde of Keswick was tempted by her desire for St. Herbert (a hermit who lived on the island in Derwent Water which now bears his name). The devil told her to ask the undying trout for two of their scales, which she did and wore them on a chain around her heart. However, the chain broke, and Ermengarde was found drowned in the River Greta.'

'The Tarns of Lakeland' – W. Heaton Cooper

At the same time, pressurised streams, trapped between the ice and rock, weather faults and weaknesses, deepening the surface further. As the temperature rises, the ice melts to reveal its awesome work. It loosens its grip on the rock carried on its surface and entombed within, scattering smooth mounds and snaking embankments across the new landscape. Over time water collects in the scoured hollows and behind these twisting natural dams and tarns are born.

Away from the volcanic rock of the Lake District the gentle contours show that ice sheets had an easier passage, scouring wide areas more evenly. When the ice melted large amounts of material were deposited on the newly exposed surface. On limestone, where water readily drains, tarns formed in the few places where this glacial debris was sufficiently impermeable to prevent water seeping away.

Ice sheets also covered the North Pennines, but since the end of the ice age layers of peat have formed over the initial post-glacial landscape. Slopes tend to be gentle and the high rainfall means soils often become waterlogged, allowing the development of tarns or intermittent pools.

Harrop Tarn

A TALE OF TWO TARNS

blea tarn

blelham tarn

	blea tarn	blelham tarn
Where?	On the eastern slopes of High Street	Just west of Windermere
How high?	482m	46m
How deep?	63m	15m
What kind of rocks?	Resistant Borrowdale volcanic rock	Softer shales and slates
How was it formed?	In the bowl left by a cirque glacier	In an ice-scooped hollow dammed by moraines and material carried in glacial streams
Which means...	• The rocks in the screes and moraines break down slowly, releasing few nutrients and little silt into the soil or tarn	• The softer rocks produced a fine glacial debris, richer in nutrients and left in generous amounts by the retreating ice
	• Soils are thin and acid	• The more fertile soils support pasture and woodland
	• The water is low in nutrients, supporting only a limited and specialised range of algae and larger plants and the water is very clear	• Nutrients leach into the water from the surrounding soil, supporting a rich variety of algae and larger plants. The water is green and murky at times
	• The shoreline is rocky and little changed since the glacier melted. Lack of silt, low temperatures and strong winds limit water edge and floating-leaved plants	• The tarn's low, sheltered position and the silt build-up on its bed allow a thick fringe of vegetation to flourish along its shore

TARN TERRORS

Bladderworts

There are many fascinating plants associated with the tarns of the fells, but none more curious than an extraordinary rare carnivorous plant called bladderwort. There are about 200 species of bladderwort in the world, ranging in size from a few centimetres to a metre long.

All bladderworts are rootless. They have main stems from which lacy, often complex leaves grow. Bladderwort flowers are yellow and have two lip-like petals of about equal size. The flowers grow on long stalks that emerge several inches above the water.

Bladderwort manufactures food from sunlight and simple chemicals it can get from pond water, but to supplement its supply of nutrients it has adopted a carnivorous way of life. As its name suggests it traps and digests tiny animals in bladders which are attached at regular intervals along its leaves.

Dragonflies

Beneath the tarn surface fearsome predators lurk. Dragonfly larvae hide amongst the water weeds. They eat by shooting out a jawed structure from under the head. This allows them to catch other insects or small fish and tadpoles disproportionate to their size, locking onto their prey with sharp jaws.

Dragonfly larvae escape from predators by darting backwards, propelled by water jets out of the gut. On the stems of emergent plants in summertime you may see these larvae crawling out of the water. Here their outer skin splits and the adult insects emerge in all their glory. They do this under the cover of darkness, whilst potential predators sleep.

Adult dragonflies with their brilliant coloured bodies and shining wings are an impressive sight when seen resting on tarn side vegetation. They are no less voracious than their larvae devouring large numbers of insects, including members of their own kind.

Medicinal Leeches

One of the biggest and most spectacular 'worms' living in tarns is the medicinal leech. This is the only British leech capable of sucking blood from humans. Because it is equipped with an anticoagulant it has been used to prevent blood clotting as well as to treat all kinds of ailments, from headaches to stomach aches.

Medicinal leeches were probably once widespread in Cumbrian tarns but are now reduced to only 35 sites, possibly due to over collection from the wild. In 1833 alone, France imported 42 million leeches. Wordsworth referred to this decline in his poem *Resolution and Independence*:

He with a smile did then his words repeat;
And said that, gathering Leeches, far and wide
He travelled; stirring thus about his feet
The waters of the Pools where they abide.
'Once I could meet with them on every side;
But they have dwindled long by slow decay;
Yet still I persevere, and find them where I may.'

Dragonfly larva

Adult black darter dragonfly

Bladderwort

Medicinal leech

A Taste of Tarns: **I n n o m i n a t e   T a r n**

L o c a t i o n : On the narrow Haystacks ridge between Buttermere and Ennerdale
A l t i t u d e : 525m
D e p t h : ~1 m
A r e a : 0.004 km^2
p H : 4.9
O r i g i n : A basin formed as an ice sheet moved over the area scouring hollows in the surface which filled with water
G e o l o g y : Lies on the hard resistant Borrowdale volcanic rocks
T a r n T a l k : This shallow tarn with its irregular shoreline and islands occupies a elevated position between Buttermere and Ennerdale with fine views over to Pillar and Great Gable. It is popular with walkers and well-known for being Alfred Wainwright's favourite tarn. It is a peaty tarn with a thick layer of sediment at its base. Its other name is 'Loaf Tarn' which may have been inspired by the tufts of grass and heather which break through the surface and resemble loaves. Water boatmen, caddisflies and common hawker dragonflies have all been found here.

Tarn soup

Water is a great medium for life. Plants thrive in tarns where the water provides them with support and a ready supply of dissolved nutrients from the rain and washed in from surrounding soils. Animals can easily float on or in water and move around with ease, swimming below, or even walking and skating on the surface.

Tarns act like a giant mixing bowl, acquiring chemicals from many sources. Weathering and erosion release minerals from rocks, rainfall deposits dust and particles from the air and washes soluble substances from soils. Oxygen, constantly supplied from the atmosphere and from plants during photosynthesis, is dissolved in the water. These ingredients are blended in the tarn producing a kind of 'nutrient soup', which forms the staple diet of the microscopic organisms that are fundamental to the tarn food chain.

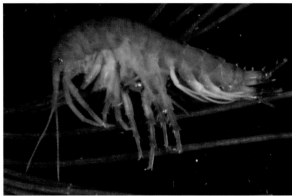

Water shrimp (top) and water snail (bottom).
The distribution of some species is closely linked to the
level of certain chemicals in the water

With so many tarns in Cumbria, it is not surprising that not all the soups taste the same. Tarns are sometimes classified by the level of nutrients in their waters, or if you like, the ingredients in the soup. At one end of the scale are tarns that are poor in nutrients. These are called **'oligotrophic'** tarns and include most of the tarns in the central fells, whose hard, resistant volcanic rock and thin upland soil provide few ingredients. Waters of these mountain tarns are like consommés: mainly thin and clear, compared with the other richer tarns. Acidity is another measure of the quality of tarn water and the waters of upland tarns tend to be more acidic.

Tarns talk

An American friend once asked what came to mind on viewing lakes or ponds; was it purely scientific? Hardly; you can't miss the beauty of most water bodies, large or small, and be saddened at those ill-used with rubbish, or filled in as wasteland. His mistaken view was, 'seen one lake, seen them all', but then Minnesota was the 'Land of Lakes'!

I began my research studies on the history of Blea Tarn, on the col between Little and Great Langdale. The accumulating lake mud contains changing animal, plant and chemical relics along a timeline from glacier retreat to the present day. I went on to study Little Langdale Tarn, Elterwater and the basins of Windermere, looking at the long term changes due to changing climate, land use, the influence of local mining and the effect of the local sewage works. To understand the evidence of the past, you must know the present.

Cumbria's range of waterbodies is exceptional, due to our location and geological diversity, ranging from acidic granite and bog pools to alkaline limestone ones. Present tarns are the product of a varied landscape history. I have tried to collect samples from all of them and there is a lot of work remaining. There is no such thing as a typical tarn and there is interest in every one as you look closer and closer.

Elizabeth Haworth, Windermere

Water boatman

Styhead Tarn, one of Cumbria's special nutrient-poor tarns, where the rare awlwort can be found

The combination of acidity and lack of nutrients is rare in freshwater in England. This makes such tarns particularly important increasing the value of the relatively few species which have adapted to their harsh environment. Their clear soft water typically supports only a handful of characteristic plant species like water-starwort, quillwort, shoreweed, water lobelia and floating bur-reed.

One of the most unusual plants is awlwort, which occurs only in a handful of tarns, including Sprinkling and Styhead Tarns at the head of Borrowdale and Dock and Blea Tarns in the Armboth Fells. Another oligotrophic tarn, Red Tarn, Helvellyn, is the only tarn in which the rare fish, the schelly, occurs.

At the opposite end of the scale are more alkaline tarns. These are nutrient rich and known as **'eutrophic'** tarns, often occuring on limestone. Limestone contains compounds which promote plant growth and are easily dissolved.

In addition, tarns on limestone tend to be surrounded by more fertile soils, from which nutrients may be washed into their waters. Consequently, they contain more dissolved material; at times they are thick and cloudy, like broths. They also tend to be more alkaline and more productive, providing opportunity for a wider, less specialist range of species.

Tarn life

Tarn life is rich and varied, but much of tarn society passes by the naked eye. Tarns may seem quiet places, but at a microscopic level activity is frenetic, with millions of minute, multi-coloured plants and animals moving through water, giving tarns the buzz of an aquatic metropolis. Fuelling the underwater food chain is **'phytoplankton'**, small floating plants which include many types of algae. Algae photosynthesize, using energy from the sun to convert carbon dioxide and water into food. Aquatic animals then graze on algae in the same way that sheep feed on grass on the fells. Despite their small size, more than 1000 species of algae have been identified by scientists in Cumbria's inland waters.

Microscopic floating and swimming animals are called **'zooplankton'**. They are a range of extraordinarily-shaped creatures with intricately detailed limbs, hairs and tails protruding from tiny bodies. Even the largest are less than half the width of a pencil.

Larger plants are easier to see and many different types take advantage of the variety of conditions for growth that tarns offer. Reeds and rushes may form dense beds around tarn edges. Plants such as these cannot survive in

Tarn Tales: Lanty's Tarn

'Apparently tarn making runs in the Marshall blood, for the Patterdale branch dammed up Lanty Tarn at the south end. The main purpose was to create a permanent all-the-year-round supply of ice for their hospitable table.

"Ice Day" was quite an occasion among the dark days of winter. All the workers were given a large dinner of "tatie hash" and afterwards assembled at the tarn above. A flat bottomed boat was used, from which ice was cut into blocks and steered to the dam. These were carried into a "cold house" which consisted of three chambers and was solidly built. In the inner chamber - now walled up - was a large egg-shaped bowl and this in its turn was covered with sawdust to a thickness of three or four feet. When the ice was required in summer, two men would go up and bring it down, after sealing up the remainder.'

'The Tarns of Lakeland' - W. Heaton Cooper

A Taste of Tarns: **Mockerkin Tarn**

Location: On farmland south of Cockermouth close to the village of the same name
Altitude: 120m
Depth: 3m
Area: 0.035km^2
pH: 7.1
Origin: A lump of glacial ice became embedded in stones and rocks deposited as the glaciers retreated. This ice melted at a different rate from the main glacier leaving behind a hollow or 'kettle hole' which filled with water
Geology: A rare tarn occurring on the sandstone rocks to the west of the Lake District
Tarn Talk: Mockerkin Tarn is said to be haunted. Sir Mochar was a legendary local villain who looted the countryside on his horse Black Rook with a pack of dogs. One story tells of how he caught and killed three maidens who had tried to escape his evil clutches. When he returned to his castle he found the gatekeeper asleep. He vowed he would slay everyone inside even if it sank twenty miles deep. The legend says that it did, leading to rumours that the tarn was bottomless. The bells of the village that was drowned with the castle are said to be still heard and the tarn haunted by the ghost of Black Rook.

Natural shoreline vegetation (left) and great diving beetle (right)

very deep water, unlike floating plants, the leaves of which can sometimes be seen on or extending above the water surface. They may have their roots on the bed, like white water-lilies, or float freely like duckweed.

In deeper water and normally hidden from view are plants that live beneath the surface, rooted to the tarn bed. These submerged plants grow wholly under water, absorbing supplies of oxygen and carbon dioxide and some nutrients directly from the water. Quillwort is one submerged plant that is special to Cumbria. It is not a flowering plant, but a fern which grows in open water and reproduces by releasing spores.

Look into a tarn and it may not seem as if anything is happening. However, peer across the surface of many tarns on a still day and you will begin to see the underwater world come alive. Many tarns provide habitat for a variety of aquatic life specially adapted to survive in different parts of the tarn. Pond skaters dart across the surface hunting for insects which become trapped in the surface film. As the sun sets, immature stages of many animals rise up to split their larval skins and take to the wing. Some creatures, like the water flea, are transparent; under a microscope you can watch its heart beating and blood circulating, or follow food passing down its gut.

Tarn Lunches

PHYTOPLANKTON   WATER FLEA   INSECT LARVA   TROUT   OTTER

- Life in tarns is like a chain with creatures being dependent on one another to survive. Phytoplankton - the minute floating plants of the open water - are the first link in the chain. They harvest the energy of the sun through photosynthesis.

- Zooplankton, tiny animals such as water fleas, feed on these microscopic plants using their specially adapted legs to draw water towards them. Practically invisible to the naked eye, many of these tiny creatures can be found in every drop of tarn water.

- Insect larvae and fish, such as rudd, patrol the waters consuming the zooplankton.

- These are preyed upon by the tarns' most awesome predators, large trout and pike.

- Even these may become lunch for an occasionally visiting otter.

The place in the tarn which few people see is actually the one most full of life. On the bottom we find the larvae of many insects feeding on the dead plants and animals which drift down from above. After spending months or, in the case of some dragonflies, years in the tarn, when the time is right they ascend through the water to emerge as adults. During their brief summer they mate and lay eggs.

Tarns are home to insects like mayflies, dragonflies, water boatmen, water beetles and caddisflies, as well as many snails and worms. In spring most tarns contain the eggs of frogs, toads and newts, differentiated by how they are laid. Frogs' eggs occur in clumps, toads eggs in strings and newts lay their eggs singly attached to leaves of aquatic plants. All three of Britain's newt species occur in the tarns of the fells and the absence of fish in many tarns has aided their survival.

Brown trout are a common tarn fish. They are often very small and slow growing in acidic upland waters, but grow well where food is abundant. If you have sharp eyes you might see pike lurking in the weedy shallows, eels and perch well-camouflaged amongst vegetation and minnows, often in large shoals, in clear stony tarns.

TARN SCIENCE

Tarn Scientists

When it comes to understanding the science of Cumbria's tarns, the Freshwater Biological Association has the expertise. An independent, international membership organisation, it has been carrying out research into freshwater in the Lake District since 1929.

Based at Ferry House, adjacent to the Windermere ferry landing, it has undertaken many experiments in Lakeland's tarns, especially the nearby Blelham Tarn. In the 1960s and 70s experiments were performed here on algal control and the effects of artificial mixing of water, which has had important influences on the management of reservoirs all over the world.

It undertakes freshwater scientific research, runs conferences, produces identification keys to freshwater plants and animals and other books and houses one of the finest freshwater libraries in the world.

Tarn Volunteers

Ralph Stokoe was a keen Cumbria Wildlife Trust member who between 1975 and 1980, collected plant records for approximately 300 tarns across Cumbria. His diaries provide a valuable and extensive source of information, which now provides the focus for a new volunteer project.

In 2004 Cumbria Wildlife Trust and the Freshwater Biological Association established a small group of volunteers to re-sample some of Stokoe's tarns. Comparing today's plants and/or animals with the old records enables changing biodiversity to be monitored and to shed light on the effects of changing upland use over the last 25 years.

A database of information about tarns, containing the results of many decades of work by volunteers and scientists of several generations, is also being developed.

Tarn Sediments

Weathered rocks, local soils and organic matter are all deposited on the bed of a tarn where they accumulate and form sediments. Scientists who take cores of these sediments can read the annual records of deposited material like tree rings and investigate how the tarn and its surroundings have changed over time.

Pollen grains are well-preserved in the sediment. By identifying different sorts of pollen scientists can build a picture of how vegetation has changed around a tarn.

At Burnmoor Tarn the sediment record goes back 14,000 years and scientists have been able to build up a complete picture of when certain tree species first occurred and changes due to the impact of man. Cross-referencing with carbon-dated cores from other tarns means scientists can corroborate the history of these landscapes changes.

Tarn Shapes

The shape and size of tarns tells us a lot about how they were formed. Much of the information we have about Cumbria's tarns comes from surveys carried out by the Brathay Exploration Group. It began surveying tarns soon after World War II as part of a programme of courses in the outdoors for young people from industrial northern towns.

Soundings of tarns were made using using lead weights and hemp lines. Equipment had to be carried to the remotest tarns. The surveyors even designed their own boat, a wood and canvas folding dinghy, which could be easily transported.

Altogether some 500 young people and volunteers took part in the tarn surveys and by 1960 most of the larger tarns had been recorded. Further tarn surveys were carried out in the 1980s and now survey charts of over 50 tarns are available, shedding new light on the form of Cumbria's upland waters.

'Lund tubes' in Blelham Tarn, part of experiments on algal control and mixing in water carried out by the Freshwater Biological Association in the 1970s and 80s

y House, home of the
hwater Biological Association

A volunteer undertaking tarn survey work

Dawn at Tarn Hows

Around tarns bats can often be seen, especially at dusk, with occasional sightings of water voles or otters. Bird life of the tarns of the high fells is mostly limited to a few species, such as skylark and meadow pipit. On lower tarns like Bigland Tarn, coot, moorhen and ducks are common. If the tarn is fringed with reed beds, you may spot reed warblers and reed buntings, or sedge warblers in any adjacent scrub.

Tarn Tales: **Tarn Hows**

'A legend from the Middle Ages tells of a giant, "Gurt Will of the Tarns", who built himself a rude dwelling up there. One day the beautiful young Eva le Fleming was walking in the woods by the side of Yewdale Beck with her maid Barbara when Gurt Will burst through the trees, seized Barbara in his arms and disappeared towards the tarns. The Lady Eva raised the alarm and Dick Hawksley, a handsome young falconer to whom Barbara was betrothed, pursued them and attacked Will at a turn of the beck which was in full spate after heavy rains. Still grasping Barbara, Will defended himself as best he could, till, in desperation, he flung her, and Dick after her, into the swirling river, where both were drowned. Higher up Yewdale the le Fleming archers overtook him, and he was slain. His grave, so the tale runs, can be seen to this day between the main road and the beck'.

'The Tarns of Lakeland' – W. Heaton Cooper

Tarn swimming in Stickle Tarn

Tarns talk

There is that moment of anticipation when, after a long climb, you reach the lip of the tarn and all of a sudden this inviting stretch of water opens out in front of you. I slip in and swim out at a steady pace taking in my surroundings as I go. On reaching the far shore, I climb out, find a rock or somewhere comfortable to sit and enjoy the often unfamiliar view in the opposite direction. On the way back I really stretch out and practise my strokes, feeling glad to be alive and able to swim in such deliciously cool, clear water.

I've been swimming in the tarns from March to October for a couple of years now, and I'm hooked: I've been divebombed by black-headed gulls in Stickle Tarn (Langdale) when they thought I might venture too close to their island nests; I've swum through swathes of sedges, rushes and water horsetail and past blooms of water lobelia, water crowfoot and bogbean; and I've begun a swim in Alcock Tarn in glorious sunshine and ended it in a hailstorm. The tarns are indeed the 'eyes of the mountain' as William Heaton Cooper so accurately described them, for they mirror the mountains and the skyscapes in all their many moods.

Jane Armstrong, London

Walker on Striding Edge above Red Tarn

Tarn inspiration

There is something irresistible about the interface between land and water. Throughout history people have been drawn towards lakes and tarns and the change of landscape between the surety of *terra firma* and the mystery of water still casts a powerful spell over our minds today.

Tarns have shaped our culture and have been the inspiration for writers, poets and artists. Moss Eccles Tarn, near Hawkshead, was the setting for Beatrix Potter's *The*

Tale of Jeremy Fisher. In Arthur Ransome's *Swallows and Amazons*, Trout Tarn is said to be 'High, high on the top of the moor, a little lake in a hollow of rock and heather'. It is here that Roger falls in as he splashes around trying to grasp the fish that he and Titty had caught. Trout Tarn is thought to be Beacon Tarn, east of Coniston Water. Trout can still be caught there today.

Watendlath Tarn clearly influenced Hugh Walpole's writing. In his novel *Judith Paris*, it is mentioned so often

A Taste of Tarns: **S u n b i g g i n   T a r n**

Location: Close to Great Asby Common three and a half miles east of Orton
Altitude: 250m
Area: 0.046km^2
pH: 8.8
Origin: Uncertain, possibly formed in a basin made by an ice sheet, or a sink hole blocked by glacial deposits
Geology: One of only a handful of water bodies lying on limestone in Britain, giving it a distinctive flora
Tarn Talk: Sunbiggin Tarn is famous for its bird life, particularly its ducks. Teal and wigeon winter here and it is the only place in Cumbria where gadwall regularly breed. Tufted ducks and mallard breed in large numbers. Raptors are common including buzzard, kestrel, sparrowhawk, merlin, hen and marsh harrier, and a sighting of a rare red kite has been known. Twenty-five species of waders have been recorded here and red grouse live in the heather moorland bounding the tarn. Several species of gulls can be seen around the tarn during summer and short-eared owls frequent the area outside the breeding season. There are also a large number of more common field birds making the tarn one of the best birdwatching waters in the county.

Tarns talk

Everyone knows at least a handful of the great water bodies that epitomise the Lake District. It's hard to ignore the long, winding ribbons of Windermere and Ullswater, or not stop to admire as another glinting Lakeland jewel appears as one ascends the hillside. These, with the mountains, are the defining features that make the Lakes the Lakes.

But what of all of those other water bodies too numerous to mention? These define our rambles into the hills and punctuate our walks as landmarks, milestones and bait stops. Not being a great summit bagger, tarns can often form the centre piece of my walks. The diversity of wildlife that they bring to often denuded, desert like fellsides, adds to the attraction for those of us with an interest in natural history.

Many times these small waters can pull us off the beaten track, allowing exploration and discovery. This can mean an out and back visit to the likes of Bowscale Tarn, a tromp across wilderness to get to Blea Tarn, above Watendlath, or a navigation exercise to find Lambfoot Dub.

From popular and oft visited tarns like Easedale to the enigmatic Tarn at Leaves, the accessible Tarn Hows to the somewhat less accessible Foxes Tarn, the peaceful and tranquil other world of Dock Tarn, to the forbidding coves of Helvellyn, these small waters define the landscape as much as the mountains themselves.

Joe Murphy, Lancaster

Watendlath Tarn

that it is as familiar as a character. On one occasion he described how the tarn was 'ruffled with little grey bird's feathers that ran in flocks under the pale sun, making the whole sheet of water quiver with life'.

In 1960 William Heaton Cooper published a collection of his tarn paintings in his classic book *The Tarns of Lakeland*. 'Tarns have a peculiar habit of becoming one's own in a way that lakes do not', he writes in his introduction. 'It is wise to give them time to do this, rather than try to bag as many as possible in the shortest possible time. In this way the game of discovery can last for many years'.

Moss Eccles Tarn, immortalised in Beatrix Potter's
The Tale of Jeremy Fisher

Tarns are the perfect place for a picnic.

For Wordsworth, the solitude of the mountain pools, though desolate and forbidding, was paradoxically part of their appeal. 'There, sometimes does a leaping fish/Send through the tarn a lonely cheer;/The crags repeat the raven's croak/In symphony austere', he writes in his *Guide to the Lakes*.

The universal appeal of tarns is with us today. Whether it is picnicking, swimming, fishing, stone-skimming or just simply sitting, tarns exude a sense of perfect peace. They will always remain a place of pilgrimage for those in search of rest, seclusion and stillness.

Tarn tools

From earliest times the attraction of tarns has been practical as well as spiritual. Their waters have been the essence of life and the fuel of progress. The hand of man can be seen in many Cumbrian tarns, exploiting the water resource for industrial, domestic or agricultural purposes. When Ehenside Tarn, in Ennerdale, was drained in 1869, a unique collection of preserved artefacts was uncovered, showing that the tarn had been a focus for civilisation during Neolithic times and giving insight into how early Cumbrians lived. Among the finds were stone axe blades quarried from factory sites on Scafell and the Langdale Pikes, which local shoemakers took away and used for sharpening their knives. Other items included animal bones, wooden paddles, clubs, basins and parts of two dugout canoes.

As the influence of man increased, so did his impact on the landscape. As they are today, the tarns of the fells would no doubt have been used in agriculture; certainly the landscape around had been changed by farming long before the arrival of the Romans. Evidence from pollen trapped in the sediment of tarn beds suggests that trees once grew around many tarns at much higher altitudes than we see them today. Man's clearing of these trees

Tarn Tales: Easedale Tarn

'A unique feature is the tiny hut built during the last century upon one of the many glacial boulders that strew the valley. Its original purpose was to shelter ponies and their riders who visited the tarn when such an expedition was thought to be a considerable adventure, as it could be when skirts trailed on the ground and their owners rode side saddle. Within living memory the hut was used by one "Swanny" Wilson for providing sumptuous teas at a shilling a head. He kept the track drained and in good repair, and even carried up to the tarn a boat which he hired to visitors. During the 1930s an Irishman, Michael O'Brien, sold mineral waters there and entertained all comers with his favourite hobby, bending six inch nails with his hands into fantastic shapes - a hobby which he practised with some advantage at local fairs.'

'The Tarns of Lakeland', W. Heaton Cooper

Easedale Tarn, where there was once a hut selling teas to visitors

not only changed the landscape, but would have had a detrimental impact on local soils, increasing soil erosion and changing levels of nutrients in tarns.

Tarns were clearly a part of the Viking landscape and many of the names they gave them we still use today. Some give us clues as to their use or who owned them. Scales Tarn, under Blencathra, is derived from the Old Norse word for 'shieling' or summer pasture and Watendlath Tarn was a lake owned by Tundelau, a British survivor of the Norse colonisation. Others are simply a description of what they are like or where they are. Blea Tarn, of which there are several, is the 'dark lake', and Scoat Tarn, in Wasdale, means 'lake under the projecting crag'.

Tarns were used for power. High Dam Tarn, near Lakeside, supplied the local Stott Park Bobbin Mill, which provided wooden bobbins for the Lancashire cotton industry. Levers Water lies in a hollow under Great How Crags carved into the Coniston Fells by glacial ice. The tarn stream flows

Tarns talk

Feeling that I should contribute something towards encouraging other people to enjoy the countryside, I trained as a Lake District National Park Voluntary Warden and I was delighted to be given the task of collecting water samples from Scales Tarn, on the slopes of Blencathra, every other month.

These high tarn samples were taken as part of a long-term environmental monitoring programme going back to the early 1970s into the effects of acidification in upland catchments, and were part of a wider study including streams, lakes and precipitation, undertaken by the Centre for Ecology and Hydrology.

The first time I undertook the duty was on a February day. Snow lay thick on the ground and the gullies trapped a good metre of snow making ordinary progress rather slow. However, there are no problems usually and, after collecting the sample, I'd either make my way to the summit of Blencathra or detour to one of the adjacent fell tops before dropping the sample off at Blencathra Centre.

Thankfully acid rain is now not as big a problem as it used to be. The project has now ended, so you won't again see me dipping a plastic bottle into the tarn, not because I was thirsty, but just doing my enjoyable bit to care for this wonderful countryside.

Phil Jelfs

Scales Tarn

Red Tarn, beneath Cold Pike

through the Coppermines Valley, which is littered with the remnants of a mining industry that dates back to at least Roman times. The tarn was dammed many years ago to provide power for the mines, raising its level by several metres.

Although no working mines remain in the Coppermines Valley, Levers Water is still used by man today. Like many tarns, including Seathwaite Tarn and Hayeswater, it is used as a reservoir. Barngates Tarn, near Hawkshead, was built in the 1930s to supply water to the Drunken Duck Inn and

is much loved by anglers in pursuit of rainbow trout and brown trout.

The original Kentmere Tarn was drained in the 1830s in an unsuccessful attempt to improve local agriculture. The lake sediments were later found to be rich in diatomite. This is the siliceous remains of millions of microscopic algae called diatoms and a valuable mineral with many industrial uses. The old tarn bed was mined for nearly 40 years before health and safety factors made it uneconomic.

Pollution of tarns can result in algal bloom

Tarn futures

Tarns are easily taken for granted. They are so numerous that some of the smallest do not even have a name and the conservation value of only a handful has been recognised by legal protection. Man's activities continually modify tarns. Tarn life is held in a delicate balance, carefully adjusted to the natural chemistry and biology of its water over thousands of years. Tipping the balance either way can have catastrophic effects. Although better regulation of industries across Europe has reduced the threat, acid rain can seriously reduce the biodiversity of tarn waters.

Run-off from agriculture and waste water from sewage works can increase tarn nutrients above natural levels. Between spring and early autumn this can allow algae to multiply rapidly, leading to 'algal blooms' in enriched waters as great green masses accumulate on the surface. When the algae die more oxygen is taken from the water during their decomposition, sometimes leading to its complete removal from the deepest waters, making them virtually uninhabitable and leaving foul-smelling mud and slime on tarn beds.

Under a natural cycle, most small water bodies will gradually fill with silt and be invaded by plants, ultimately becoming woodland. However, intensive farming, afforestation and even trampling of the tarn shores by visitors are accelerating the in-filling of tarns with silt, reducing their size faster than natural processes would. Water quality has declined and in years to come tarns we value today may disappear completely.

Many of Cumbria's tarns have been artificially dammed, altering their natural shoreline. Dams will not last forever and regulations mean that decisions will need to be taken about the safety of these dams, many of which have been in place for decades and are seen by many as part of the natural scene. The implications of these decisions for landscape and nature conservation will need to be carefully considered.

A Taste of Tarns: **G r e a t R u n d a l e T a r n**

Location : High up in the North Pennines on the slopes of Dufton Fell above High Cup Nick

Altitude : 690m

Origin : Peat began forming in the North Pennines around 5000 years ago. The tarn lies on relatively flat ground where hollows in the impervious peat are deep enough to contain collecting water

Geology : The geology of Dufton Fell is a complex mixture of limestone and gritstone layers lying on top of each other like a sandwich. The tarn lies on a band of impervious gritstone

TarnTalk : Great Rundale Tarn occupies one of the most remote sites in Cumbria, high up in the North Pennines. Here are some of the most extensive stretches of blanket bog in England. The tarn lies on a plateau alongside several other tarns and pools. Its waters are slightly acidic and the surrounding blanket bog supports a number of breeding bird species including golden plover, dunlin, snipe, oystercatcher, common sandpiper and redshank.

Tarns talk

Tarns provide fantastic variety for an artist. Everything about their form speaks of contrast. They are a break in an often rugged landscape, which irresistibly draws the eye, and enhances composition. Their perfect flatness set against stark irregular lines of the fells suggests stillness, which gives an appealing restfulness to a picture.

Yet tarns are not static. Their colours change. Fells have their own hues, summer greens, autumn brown and the grey and black of rock. Although these do change, their timescale is long and their colours remain the same for days on end. Not so for tarns, which reflect the passing sky; at once blue, then silver, then grey, all of this contrasting and complementing nature's colouring of the dark earth upon which they sit.

Then the wind blows sending ripples over the surface and the tarn changes again; the sketch of sky upon the surface is spoiled. Playing above all of this is a symphony of light altering moment by moment. Appreciating this unfolding drama as you stand and watch can be hard enough, but to capture on paper often feels impossible, as you become caught up in the scene yourself. I seldom paint enjoying the warmth of bright sunshine. Outdoor art is about wrapping up against the elements and snatching a sketch between the showers. The reward for painting tarns is more than simply producing a picture, it is in knowing what you have been through to get it.

Joanna Varley, Kendal

Loughrigg Tarn

Tarn Tales: **Foxes Tarn**

'Foxes Tarn was nearly swept away altogether in the autumn of 1958. During August and September warm air from the south-west brought clouds laden with moisture. It is estimated that rainfall exceeded six inches an hour. Great grooves were carved out of the sides of Mickledore, and the gullies of Scafell and Pikes Crag funnelled an immense force of water. From the summit ridge the water tore away thousands of tons of rock and sent them down into the corrie of Foxes Tarn. The pressure of wind and water, as well as the impact of the rocks at the back of the little tarn, almost pushed it out of its basin, deepening the outlet channel and draining away most of the water. Rocks as heavy as four tons are now embedded in the mud of its former floor. A spring that fed the tarn has pushed up slabs of hardened mud that were being formed into rock. All around the mosses are green and flourishing on what was formerly the bed of the tarn.'

'The Tarns of Lakeland,' - W. Heaton Cooper

Climate change will undoubtedly have an effect on the tarns of the fells, although its impact may not be easily seen as the changes may be gradual. Many scientists are predicting wetter winters and drier summers. More rainfall in winter will mean more water running down fellsides into tarns, altering their water chemistry and potentially increasing the rate at which they silt up. Lower rainfall in summer could lead to more tarns drying up with accompanying changes in biodiversity, recreational and landscape value. Opportunities for invasive, non-native plants and animals to colonise tarns may also increase. Such species are often difficult to eradicate once they have a foothold and seriously disrupt local ecosystems.

It is difficult to predict what the future will bring for Cumbria's tarns, but man's actions will have an impact on them and bring about changes above and beyond those of natural processes. However, we know a lot about Cumbria's tarns thanks to biologists who have studied them since the middle of the last century. If we are diligent we can use this knowledge to help monitor and protect them in the future.

Further Information

BOOKS AND OTHER RESOURCES

A Natural History of the Lakes, Tarns and Streams of the
English Lake District
Geoffrey Fryer. Freshwater Biological Association.
ISBN: 0900386509
*A comprehensive and accessibly written guide to the life
and environment of water in the Lake District*

Tarns of the Central Lake District
E.Haworth, G. de Boer, I.Evans, H.Osmaston, W.Pennington,
A.Smith, P.Storey and B.Ware. Brathay Exploration Group Trust.
ISBN 0906015170
*The results of an exhaustive scientific study of nearly 50
tarns carried out over two decades*

The Tarns of Lakeland
W. Heaton Cooper. Heaton Cooper Studio, Grasmere.
ISBN: 0950115207
*A most readable account of Lakeland Tarns, illustrated
throughout with Heaton Cooper's excellent paintings*

Exploring Lakeland's Tarns: A Complete Guide
Don Blair. Lakeland Manor Press.
ISBN: 0954390415
A where-to-go what-to-see guide to the tarns

The Tarns of Lakeland (Vols 1 & 2)
John and Anne Nuttall. Cicerone Press.
ISBN:1852841710
*Description of walks to the tarns with maps and pen
drawing illustrations*

FreshwaterLife

FreshwaterLife is a website, hosted by the
Freshwater Biological Association which
provides easy access to information about
freshwater organisms and habitats. It
relies on the collaboration of experts and
enthusiasts from all over the world.
www.freshwaterlife.info

ORGANISATIONS AND SOCIETIES

Cumbria Wildlife Trust is the only voluntary
organisation devoted solely to the
conservation of wildlife and wild places in
Cumbria. For more information contact:
*Cumbria Wildlife Trust, Plumgarths, Crook
Road, Kendal, Cumbria, LA8 8LX.
Tel: 01539 816300*
www.cumbriawildlifetrust.org.uk

English Nature is the Government agency
that champions the conservation of wildlife
and natural features throughout England.
For more information contact:
*English Nature Cumbria Team, Murley Moss
Business Park, Oxenholme Road, Kendal, Cumbria, LA9 7RL.
Tel: 01539 729800*
www.english-nature.org.uk

FRESHWATER BIOLOGICAL ASSOCIATION The Freshwater Biological Association,
conducts research into all aspects
of freshwater science, particularly
ecology, and produces papers and publications on the
subject. For more information contact:
*The Freshwater Biological Association, The Ferry House,
Ambleside, Cumbria, LA22 0LP. Tel: 015394 42468*
www.fba.org.uk

Friends of the Lake District is a
landscape charity which works to
protect and enhance the countryside
of Cumbria and the Lake District. Formed in 1934 it now
has almost 7000 members. For more infomation contact:
*Friends of the Lake District, Murley Moss Business Park,
Oxenholme Road, Kendal, LA9 7SS. Tel: 01539 720788*
www.fld.org.uk